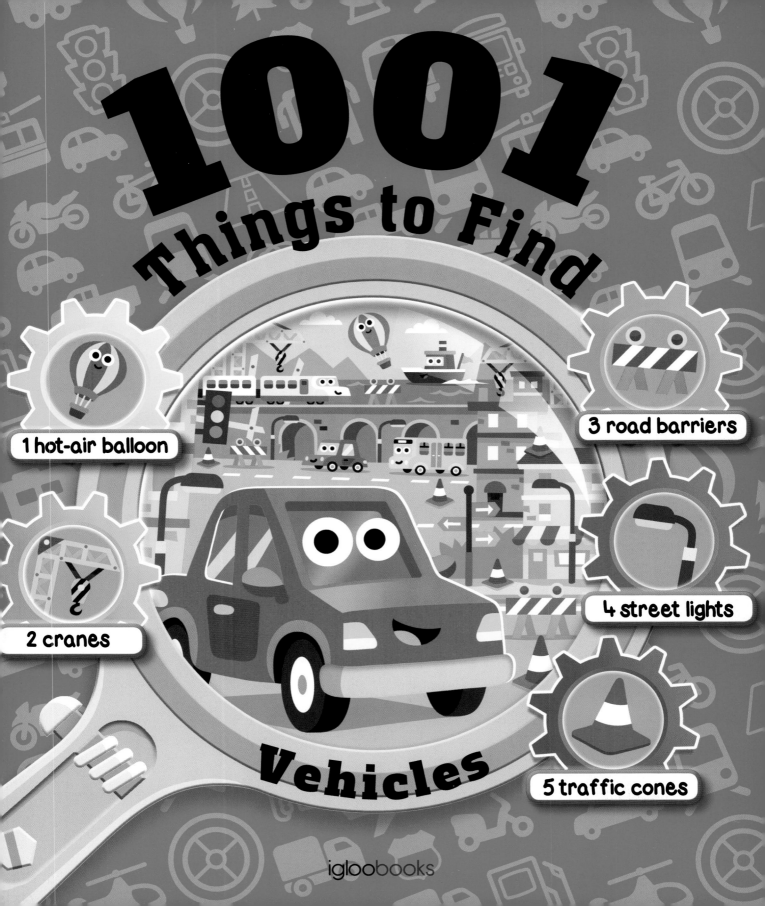

1001
Things to Find

1 hot-air balloon

2 cranes

Vehicles

3 road barriers

4 street lights

5 traffic cones

igloobooks

Can you find 1001 vehicle items?

Start your engines, it's a race to the finish line!
Red Car and Blue Car have been invited to a special street party,
but only the racing flags will lead them to its secret location.

To find each flag, they must race around the busy city to visit
all their vehicle friends, before moving on to find the next clue.

In every scene, look for Red Car, Blue Car and the racing flag that
leads them to the street party. There are over 1000 vehicle items
for you to find along the way, too, so let's get finding!

Red Car　　　　**Racing Flag**　　　　**Blue Car**

On the opposite page, see if you can spot Red Car, Blue Car and the
racing flag. Once you've found them, see if you can spot the items below, too.

2 oil cans　　　　**8 pots of paint**　　　　**11 spanners**

Rush Hour

BEEP-BEEP! Lots of vehicles whizz down the roads in the busy city, as they hurry along. Where are Red Car and Blue Car? Find the racing flag, too.

 **1 limousine**

 **4 benches**

 **5 street lights**

 **6 traffic lights**

 **7 street signs**

 **8 bins**

 **9 newspapers**

 **10 banana skins**

 **11 road barriers**

 **13 purple butterflies**

Squeaky Clean

Super sports cars, muddy trucks and more get clean among the bubbles at the car wash. Spot Red Car and Blue Car, plus the racing flag.

5 hoses

6 purple brushes

8 buckets

12 sponges

15 soap bars

To the Rescue!

In an emergency, ambulances, fire engines, police cars and all their friends rush to help. Find Red Car, Blue Car and the racing flag, too.

5 first-aid kits

6 donuts

8 fire extinguishers

12 police radios

15 gold coins

Building Crew

Diggers, bulldozers, cranes and more all work hard on the site. Spot Red Car and Blue Car visiting them. Where is the racing flag?

1 wrecking ball

4 ladders

5 piles of rubble

6 yellow boots

7 yellow hard hats

8 spades

9 pipes

10 building site birds

11 orange cones

13 red bricks

Sky High

Watch as the planes, helicopters and other flying vehicles hover overhead. Find Red Car and Blue Car, then spot the racing flag.

5 purple banners

6 paper planes

8 dragonflies

12 leaves

15 feathers

Tooting Trains

All aboard for some countryside trainspotting. Clickety-clack! Find Red Car, Blue Car and the racing flag, as the trains speed through the tunnels.

5 train signals

6 suitcases

8 plastic cups

12 whistles

15 tickets

Fun on the Farm

Come down to the farm where the tractors, combine harvesters and ploughs are hard at work. Spot Red Car and Blue Car, plus the racing flag.

1 windmill

4 milk urns

5 wheelbarrows

6 apple trees

7 pitchforks

8 hay bales

9 baby chicks

10 lettuces

11 carrots

13 white daisies

Super Skating

Ride the ramps with the skateboards and scooters, as they jump and spin in the air. Find Red Car and Blue Car, then spot the racing flag.

5 helmets

6 basketballs

8 roller skates

12 pairs of headphones

15 pink ice creams

Surf's Up!

Hit the beach with the jet ski, dinghy, surfboards and all their friends for some fun in the sun. Find Red Car, Blue Car and the racing flag, too.

5 snorkels

6 pairs of sunglasses

8 flippers

12 sandcastles

15 bottles of suncream

Sunset Sailing

Down at the docks, the ferries, ships and their other boat friends are setting sail. Can you find Red Car, Blue Car and the racing flag?

1 lighthouse

4 oars

5 buoys

6 anchors

7 sailor hats

8 telescopes

9 life rings

10 ropes

11 seagulls

13 stripy fish

Monster Trucks

Watch as these mighty machines perform the most daring tricks in their spectacular stadium. Spot Red Car and Blue Car, then find the racing flag.

5 hot dogs

6 firework displays

8 mud tracks

12 popcorn buckets

15 shooting stars

Fab Funfair

The roller coaster carriages go WOO-HOO! The bumper cars go CRASH! Find Red Car and Blue Car, then can you find the racing flag?

5 giant teddies

6 coconuts

8 cupcakes

12 rubber ducks

15 burgers

Roaring Racers

Rev your engines! Can you spot Red Car and Blue Car zooming round the track? Then find the final racing flag among the speedy vehicles.

1 lightning flag

4 oil spills

5 purple speakers

6 megaphones

7 racing bees

8 oil drums

9 stopwatches

10 pairs of goggles

11 tyres

13 red racing caps

Street Party

Spot Red Car and Blue Car celebrating with their friends, after arriving at the party. There are no more racing flags to find. What else can you see?

1 celebration cake

4 party horns

5 rosettes

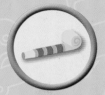

6 trophies

7 screwdrivers

8 spotty balloons

9 pairs of pliers

10 yellow flags

11 party hats

13 pieces of cog confetti

Congratulations! You helped Red Car and Blue Car make it all the way to the Street Party. Can you find each of these items in every scene, too?

A red and yellow kite

A pink bike

A bunch of keys

A racing pigeon

A toolbox

A roller-skating mouse

A no-entry sign

A bunch of balloons

Were you looking closely? Go back and see if you can spot which scene each of these characters is hiding in.

A dinghy

An orange scooter

A snail

A scarecrow